Psalm 121 © Mary Fleeson / www.lindisfarne-scriptorium.co.uk 2020

Blessed is he who comes in the name of the Lord

Psalm 118 © Mary Fleeson / www.lindisfarne-scriptorium.co.uk 2020

THE HEAVENS DECLARE THE GLORY OF GOD

Psalm 74 © Mary Fleeson / www.lindisfarne-scriptorium.co.uk 2020

HAVE MERCY ON US LORD HAVE MERCY ON US

Psalm 123 © Mary Fleeson / www.lindisfarne-scriptorium.co.uk 2020

Psalm 30 © Mary Fleeson / www.lindisfarne-scriptorium.co.uk 2020

I WILL GIVE THANKS LORD ♡ TO YOU

WITH ALL MY HEART

Psalm 9 © Mary Fleeson / www.lindisfarne-scriptorium.co.uk 2020

O GOD MAKE YOUR FACE SHINE ON US

Blessed Are Those whose hope is in the Lord their God

PRAISE BE TO THE LORD TO GOD OUR SAVIOUR WHO DAILY BEARS OUR BURDENS

Psalm 144 © Mary Fleeson / www.lindisfarne-scriptorium.co.uk 2020

Psalm 89 © Mary Fleeson / www.lindisfarne-scriptorium.co.uk 2020